WELCOME TO PIRATES OF THE MYSTIC SEAS

Your journey to becoming a comic artist has begun. You will absolutely enjoy this easy to follow 4-step instruction book and be well on your way to becoming a drawing genius. So grab your paper and pencil and let's get started!!!

Things you will need:

Pencil

Eraser

Paper

Black ink pen

Things you may want to use:

Scrap paper

Pencil crayons

Markers

Remember to press lightly when drawing, to make your extra lines easier to erase when you are finished.

STEP 1: LAYOUT OF YOUR CHARACTERS

First lightly draw or trace the outlines of these characters. Start by drawing the blue lines and then add in the red lines. This will give you the basic outline of your characters.

STEP 2: DEFINING YOUR CHARACTERS

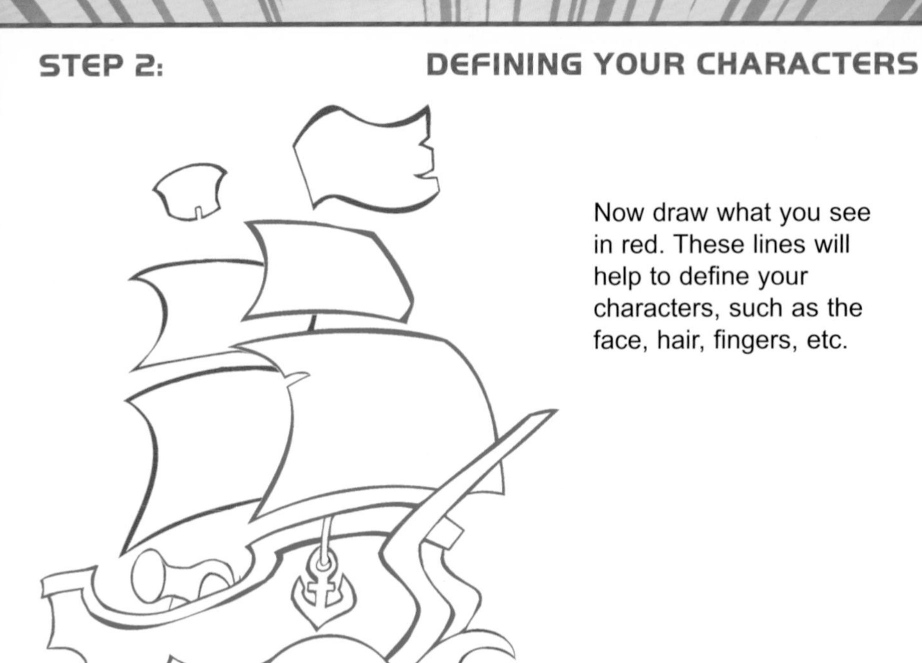

Now draw what you see in red. These lines will help to define your characters, such as the face, hair, fingers, etc.

STEP 3: DETAILING YOUR CHARACTERS

Now that you have finished the bigger details for your characters, you are going to add in the smaller details.

Draw what you see here in red.

STEP 4: INKING YOUR CHARACTERS

After you've finished drawing your characters, use a black inked pen to trace over the lines that you need and then erase any extra lines.

Use these 4 steps while drawing all the characters in this book.

COLORING YOUR CHARACTERS

When coloring your characters start by using the lightest color as your base and then add darker colors for shading.

You can use pencil crayons or markers to color your characters.

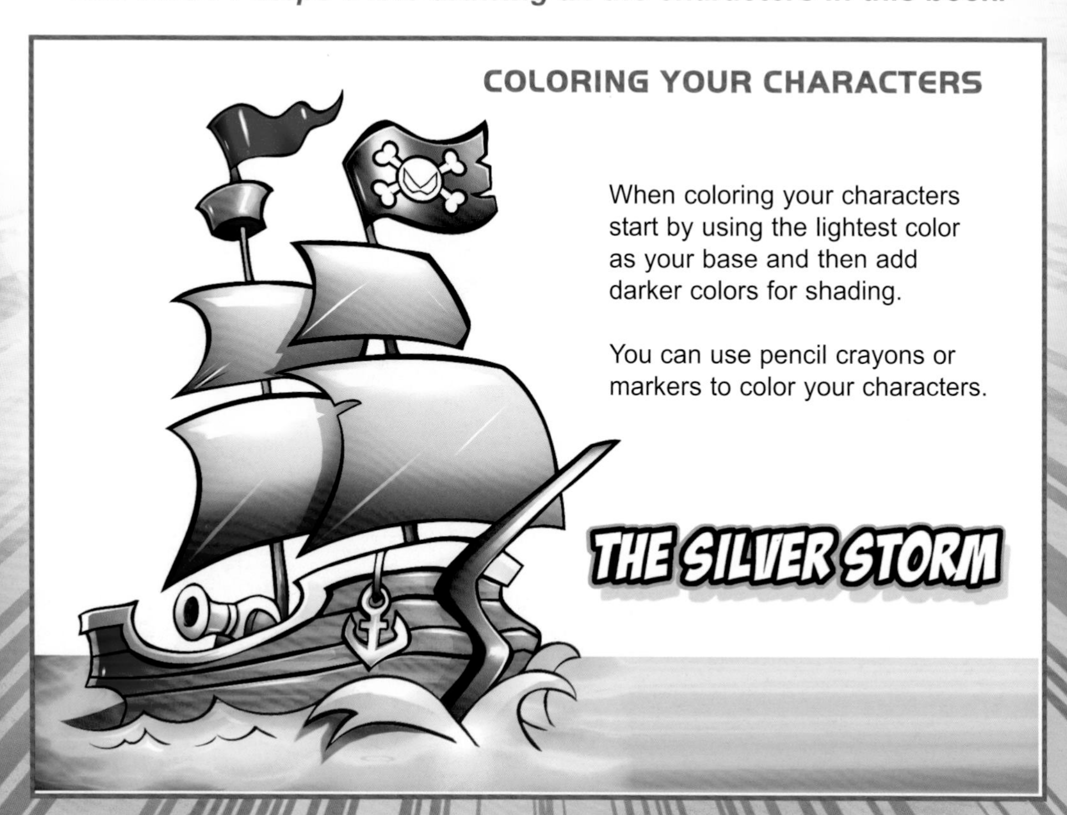

CAPTAIN SILAS

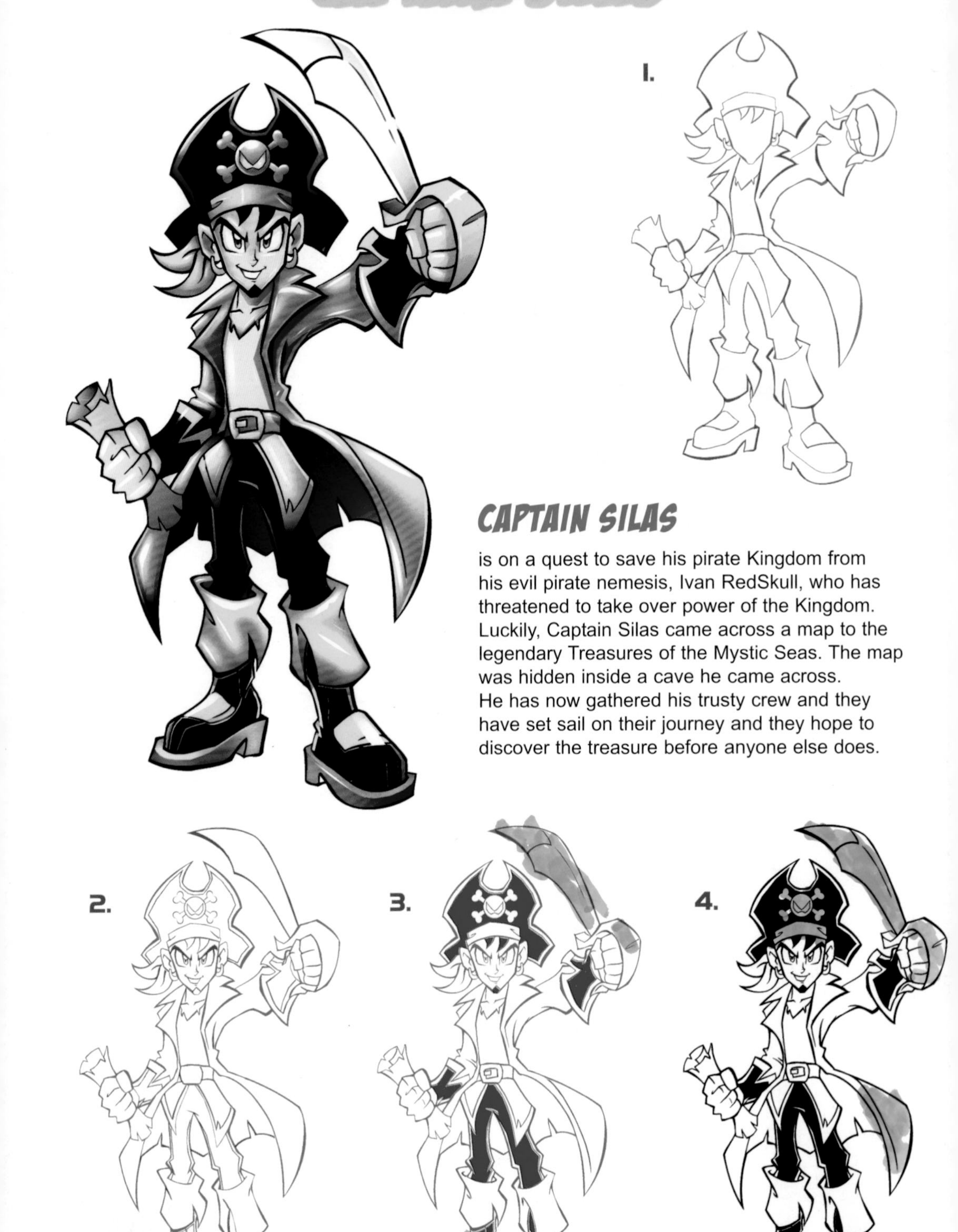

CAPTAIN SILAS

is on a quest to save his pirate Kingdom from his evil pirate nemesis, Ivan RedSkull, who has threatened to take over power of the Kingdom. Luckily, Captain Silas came across a map to the legendary Treasures of the Mystic Seas. The map was hidden inside a cave he came across.
He has now gathered his trusty crew and they have set sail on their journey and they hope to discover the treasure before anyone else does.

JACK "GOLD BRICK"

JACK A.K.A. GOLD BRICK

is Captain Silas' first mate. They have been best friends since they were young lads. He is one of strongest pirates of the Mystic Seas. Although he may look scary in appearance, he actually is very kind. Being very strong will be helpful when they find the treasure because they will have to lug it back through the jungles to their ship.

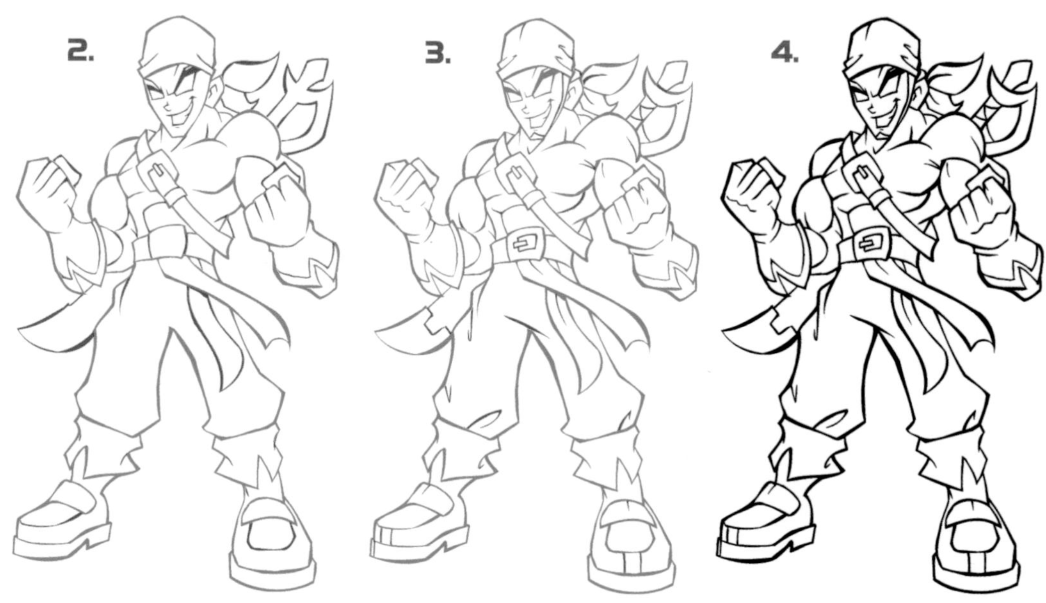

"THE TWINS" CHARLOTTE

Charlotte and Charlie Hodgins are the great granddaughters of the most famous pirate of the Mystic Seas, Captain Charles Hodgins. They are the best swordswomen in all of the Mystic Seas. They use their wits and wisdom to play mind tricks on people.

CHARLOTTE

is the sail maker. Her duties on board The Silver Storm ship are being in charge of all the fabrics and canvasses such as the sails, flag, and hammocks. In the case that any of these are damaged in the unpredictable weather conditions of the seas during a voyage, she will repair them.

AND CHARLIE

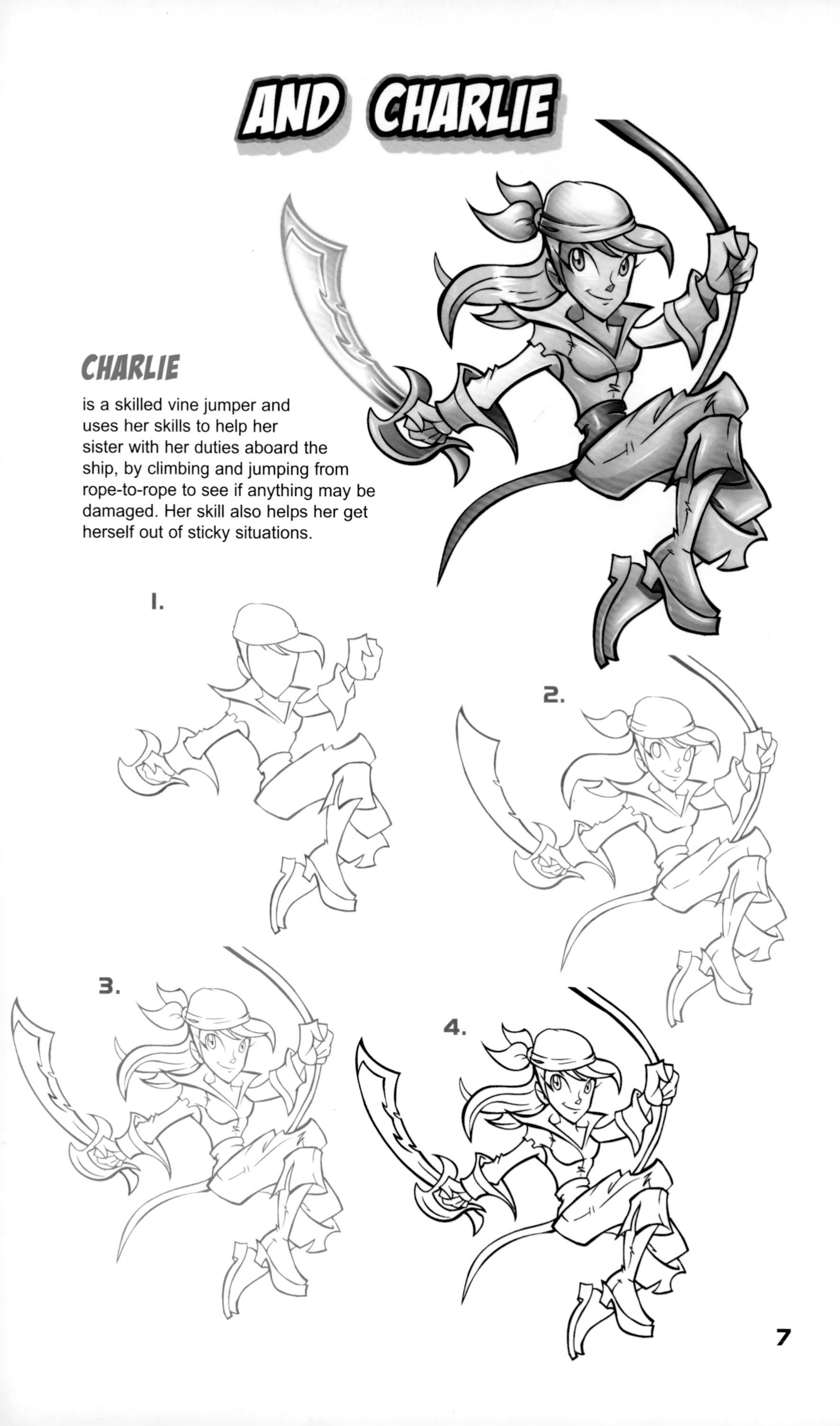

CHARLIE

is a skilled vine jumper and uses her skills to help her sister with her duties aboard the ship, by climbing and jumping from rope-to-rope to see if anything may be damaged. Her skill also helps her get herself out of sticky situations.

GAVIN

GAVIN

is the ship master. He is in charge of navigation and the sailing of the ship. He directs the course and looks after the maps and instruments used for navigation. Due to the maps being sometimes inaccurate or hard to read, he has laid trust in Jewel the mermaid to help guide them to the treasure. He was taught by his legendary uncle Captain BlueSkull of the ways of the sea and sailing. His uncle taught him writing and how to read a map, making Gavin one of the most valuable people aboard the ship.

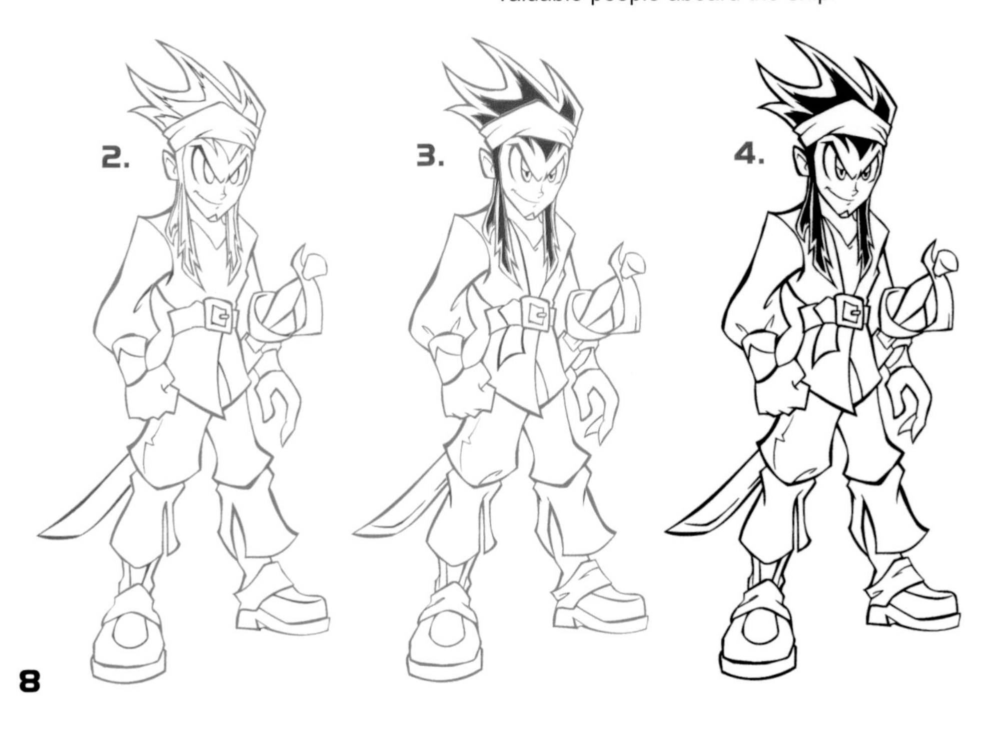

ROSE

1.

is a very skilled pirate and she has known Silas since she was a baby. He's like a brother to her and he has always looked out for her. Now it is her turn to help him and the pirate Kingdom. Aboard the ship she is known as The Boatswain---she supervises and monitors the maintenance of the vessel. She is responsible for inspecting the ship and its sails and ropes every day and reports their state to the Captain. She is also in charge of all deck activities, including weighing and dropping the anchor, and the handling of the sails.

2.

3.

4.

JEWEL

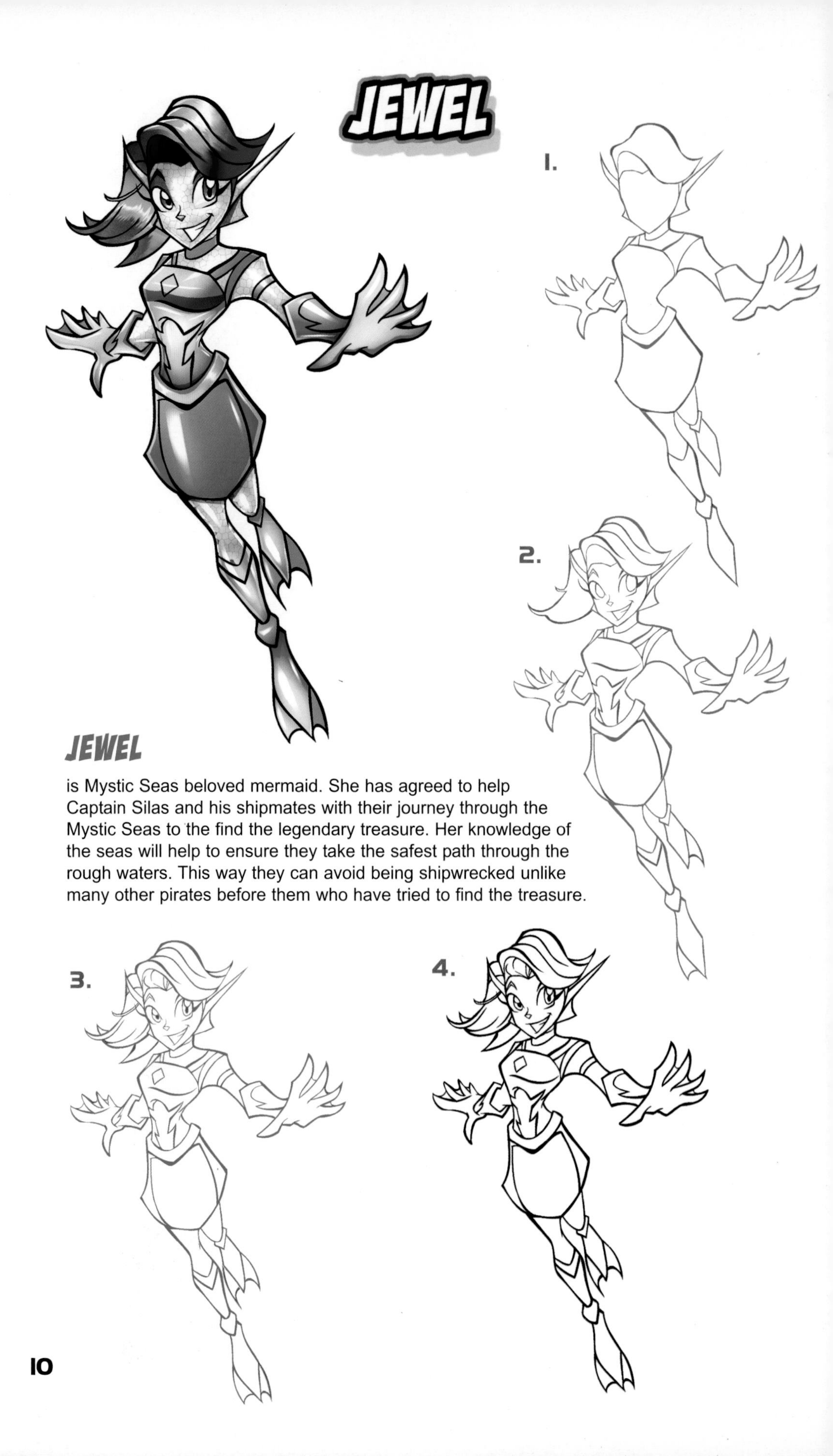

JEWEL

is Mystic Seas beloved mermaid. She has agreed to help Captain Silas and his shipmates with their journey through the Mystic Seas to the find the legendary treasure. Her knowledge of the seas will help to ensure they take the safest path through the rough waters. This way they can avoid being shipwrecked unlike many other pirates before them who have tried to find the treasure.

JAMES

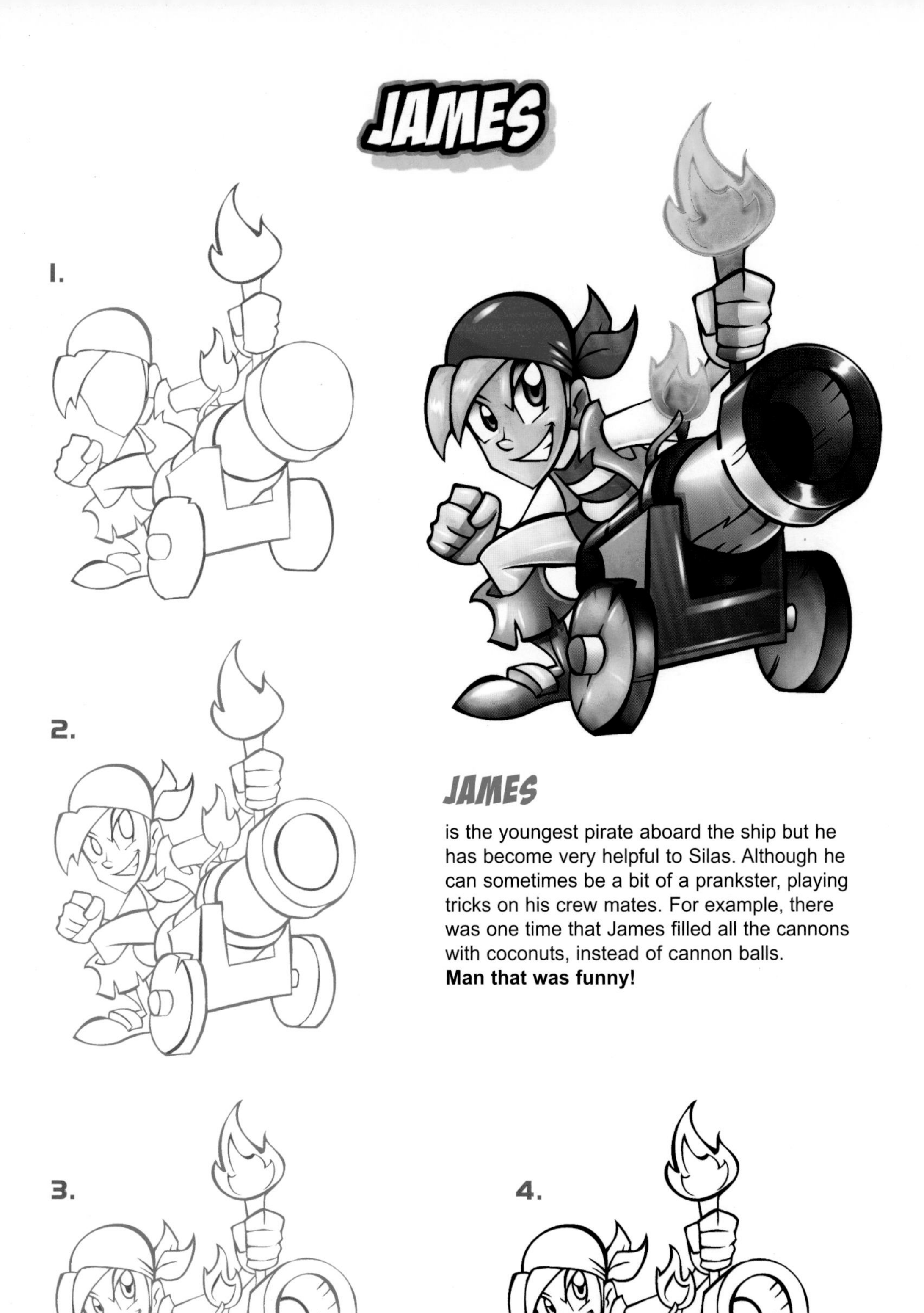

JAMES

is the youngest pirate aboard the ship but he has become very helpful to Silas. Although he can sometimes be a bit of a prankster, playing tricks on his crew mates. For example, there was one time that James filled all the cannons with coconuts, instead of cannon balls. **Man that was funny!**

3.

4.

LOCKS

Locks

the pirate parrot has been secretly spying on Silas and his crew for months. He was asked to do so by the evil pirate, Ivan RedSkull in order to save his tail after being caught trying to steal some of the evil pirate's booty.

Locks befriended Silas and made it look like he was going to help him. But instead he has double-crossed Silas and informed Ivan about all of Silas' plans. Locks has even made a copy of the treasure map which he carved into the side of his telescope for RedSkull so that he can find the fortune for himself.

EVIL PIRATE CAPTAIN IVAN REDSKULL

EVIL PIRATE: IVAN REDSKULL

is one of the scariest and most feared pirates of the Mystic Seas because he is over 6 feet tall and very powerful. After being informed by Locks that Silas has discovered a hidden map to the legendary Treasures of the Mystic Seas, he has gathered his own crew of evil misfits and ordered Locks to make him a copy of the map. In this way, he can find the treasure first and use it to become the richest and most powerful pirate of the Mystic Seas.

THE SCAVENGER

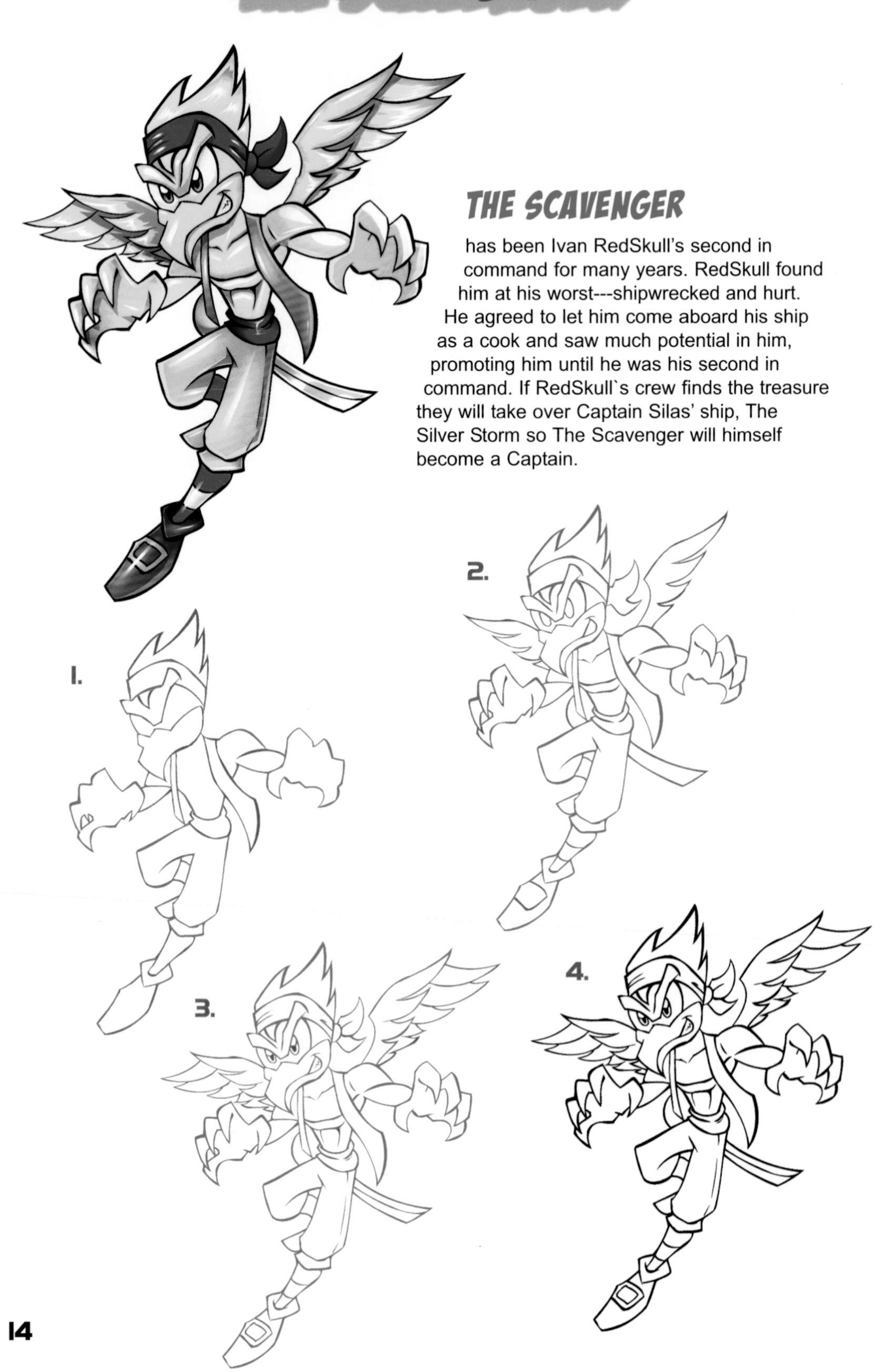

THE SCAVENGER

has been Ivan RedSkull's second in command for many years. RedSkull found him at his worst---shipwrecked and hurt. He agreed to let him come aboard his ship as a cook and saw much potential in him, promoting him until he was his second in command. If RedSkull`s crew finds the treasure they will take over Captain Silas' ship, The Silver Storm so The Scavenger will himself become a Captain.

MAD MONKEY

MAD MONKEY

was given his name because he is very unpredictable. With his small size he is able to manoeuvre around and under things most pirates can not, making him very valuable to RedSkull. He is very fast and a sneaky thief as well, so if they can just get to the treasure first, Mad Monkey can sneak in and snatch it.

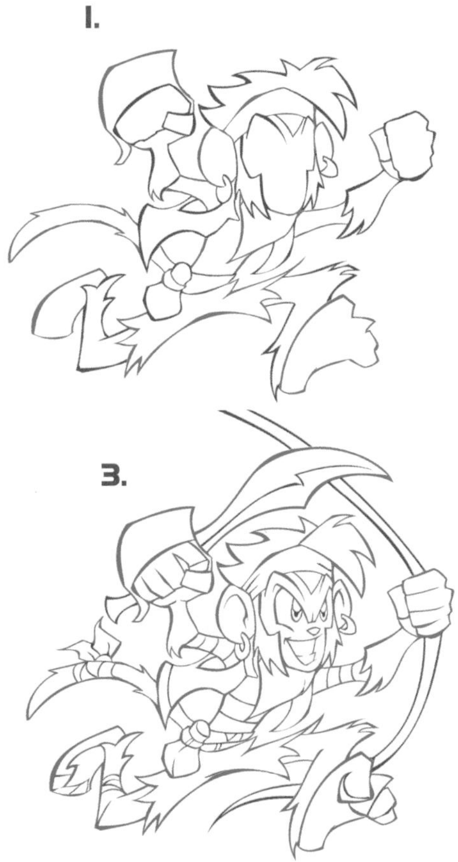

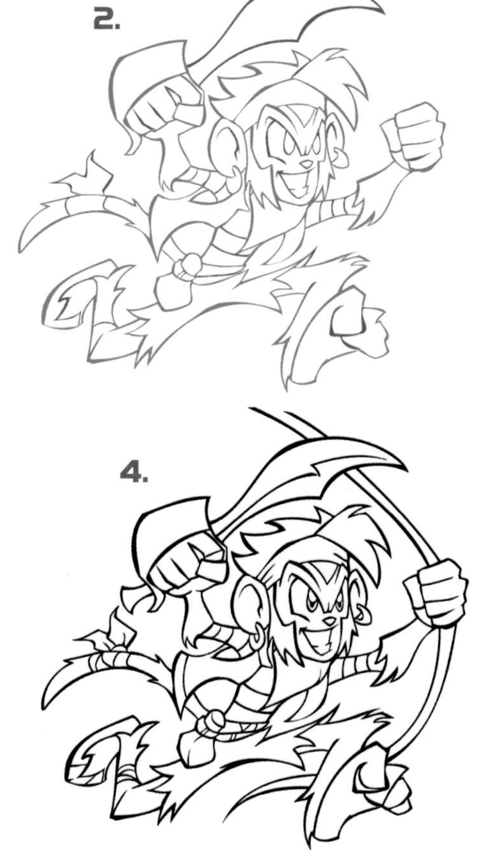

THE CROC

THE CROC

has been working with RedSkull for just a short time but he has proven himself extremely loyal to him and has gained his respect. He is incredibly strong and he is also one of the best swordsmen ever known.

LADY TYGRESS

LADY TYGRESS

has a fierce and courageous temper making her a reliable crew member for Ivan. She has helped bring a lot of wealth and power to him since she asked to be part of his pirate crew. She also has special inside information about one of the crew members aboard Silas' ship because she was once crew mates with Gavin. Although her loyalties lie with RedSkull, she has been thinking about overthrowing him and taking over his ship and crew by offering them a larger cut from their pirate findings.

Captain Silas has never really fully trusted his parrot friend Locks. Thinking that he might be double-crossing him and his crew, he devised a plan to make sure any of the information he might be giving to the evil pirate, Ivan RedSkull, was false. Captain Silas also made a fake map and left it out knowing that the bird would somehow make a copy of it and give it to Ivan.

Unfortunately for the Evil Captain Ivan RedSkull and his crew, they laid too much trust in their sidekick parrot, Locks. The entire crew have now ended up shipwrecked and stranded on a deserted island far, far away from the treasure and Captain Silas' pirate Kingdom.

At last Captain Silas and his crew have found the legendary Treasures of the Mystic Seas. They have become the most famous and richest pirates to have ever lived and plan to share their wealth with the whole Kingdom.

The End.

Freeze DNA
Design & Advertising

We strive to change the lives of young people and lift their spirits. With this very fun and exciting way of learning we hope to encourage children and youth to continue reading, writing and drawing their favorite characters.

Freeze DNA Team *Anthony Stanberry, Jermaine Smith, Justin Stanberry and Sylvia Stanberry Smith*

If you enjoyed *Pirates Of The Mystic Seas* then you will love all of our other Freeze Kids comic books!!!

To purchase any of our other books visit our web store ***now!***

www.freezekidscomicbooks.com

All Freeze Kids Books are *$5 each*

New
The Golden Dragon

New
Sugar And Spice

New
I Love To Doodle 2
Our Amazing Race